C000052769

This book is dedicated to my father
Mr Malcolm MacPherson
& to my fiancée's father
Mr Bill Carlyle

Keepers

of the Light

Malcolm MacPherson

Copyright in all countries signatory to the Berne Convention
All rights reserved

First Edition   -   2009

Whilst the author has taken care in compiling this book, the Publishers do not hold themselves responsible for any inaccuracies which may have crept in.

ISBN 978-1-84927-011-3

© 2009 BROWN, SON & FERGUSON, LTD.
4-10 Darnley Street, Glasgow, G41 2SD
Made & Printed in Great Britain

INTRODUCTION

There are well over 200 Lighthouses positioned around Scotland's most breathtaking and energetic coastline. From the Solway Firth, throughout the Inner and Outer Hebrides, Pentlands Firth, Orkney and Shetland Islands, Moray Firth's, Tay's and Forth's estuaries.

On a summer holiday with my parents, we stayed in the coastal town Arbroath. The Arbroath signal tower originally a Shore Station until 1955 built for the operational purposes of the Bell Rock lighthouse. Accommodating magnificently overlooking across the North Sea, Completed in 1813, which has now become a museum. It was from here that I imagined what it must be like to live and work on a lighthouse station.

Thomas Smith, 1752-1814 born in Broughty Ferry, Dundee, son of a ship's captain was at the forefront of lighthouse development in its first commencement. When addressed by the Commissioners of Northern Lighthouses, a corporate body of men of the legal establishment, to acquire four suitable locations across various parts of Scotland. Kinnaird Head 1787, Mull of Kintyre 1788, North Ronaldsay 1789, and Eileen Glas 1789.

After Thomas Smith retired from lighthouse engineering, his young son-in-law, Robert Stevenson (1772-1850, born in Glasgow) was in progression to Smith, became the newly appointed Chief Engineer for the new Northern Lighthouse Board. Established by an act of parliament in 1786, the General Lighthouse Authority, for Scotland and the Isle of Man. Collecting "light-dues", or fess for the revenue and maintenance within the service, in return providing the sea-fearers safe navigational passage in which ship-owners would levy so much by passing any of her lights paying per tonnage.

Their Motto, *"In Salutem Omnium"* (For the Safety of All).

In 1811, Robert Stevenson achieved what some must have thought was the impracticable, his greatest commendation, finally accomplished by completing the works of a tower that still stands in great paramount even to this very day.

The "Bell Rock Lighthouse" positioned somewhat 12 miles from Arbroath.

Built on a precariously rocky reef (Inchcape) it took four year's for its completion From, 1807-1811.

It cemented his union in the eyes of the engineering world.

Different personnel variations used in the establishment of each lighthouse were, Principal Lighthouse Keeper, Assistant, Supernumerary, Relief, Occasional, Local Attendants and Retained. Before Automation, there were predominantly two types of lighthouse stations, Rock and Shore. A Shore Station designated a (PLK), two Assistants and their families.

Rock Stations a (PLK) and two assistants, Island Stations had (PLK) with families.

Fog signal stations would have a (PLK) and sometimes two or three Assistants with 24-hour guardianship. Stations unapproachable by road, the attending boatmen usually local Fisherman where introduced to the service.

In 2011, the "Bell Rock Lighthouse" will be commemorating its 200th Anniversary.

The Stevenson's family have managed to accumulate a colossal 97 lighthouses across Scotland and the Isle of Man 1797-1938.

All standing admirably soaring above the face of adversity, enduring precise engineering, exhaustive labouring, hostile weather conditions, inadequate admittance, and basic raw materials..

Maybe it is the whole idea of solitude, the ambience of Seasonal colours, evading throughout this beautiful rugged Scottish coastline.

The Fair Isle South Lighthouse was the last Scottish manned lighthouse automated on 31st of March 1998.

I would like to add my thanks to Lorna Hunter, the Information Officer at the Northern Lighthouse Board, for all the assistance she has given me with the research in the writing of this book.

Malcolm MacPherson

A special reflection for the men that staffed these iconic structures:
"Keepers of the Light"

CONTENTS

Ardnamurchan Lighthouse
Argyllshire

Positioned on a ragged rock face on the westerly point of the British mainland. Deriving from (Scottish Gaelic: Aird Nam Murchan: meaning hill or land of the great sea) an area of unspoilt beauty with wildlife in abundance.

Alan Stevenson, born in Edinburgh 1807-1865, Alan contributed to 12 lighthouses from 1843-1853, he was the eldest of four brothers.

His father Robert Stevenson was the Chief Engineer in the Stevenson's family Household, reigning a period in centre of operations from 1797-1843.

A Shore Station Ardnamurchan lighthouse established in 1849, designed by engineer Alan Stevenson.

Ardnamurchan lighthouse took three years for its completion, be fitting the surrounding landscape, the oil light first exhibited on the 5th of October 1849, the two lighthouse keepers appointed in charge where paid a yearly payment of £18.00.

The materials quarried from the island of Earraid of the Ross of Mull; the structure is grey-pink granite flagstone circular tower, with 5 integrated windows, 35 metres in height, at the base a hemispherical single-storey building, exemplify Egyptian stonework architecture, tapering just below the lantern, first ever used in the structure of lighthouse engineering on the British Isles.

To reach the lamp room you have to ascend 152 steps, when upon entering the light, embraced with overwhelming panoramic views across the stunning contiguous islands of Coll, Muck, Rhum, Eigg, and the Atlantic Ocean beyond.

Robert Hulme was the contractor for building the lighthouse cost £13,738.

The living accommodation one-storey keepers' cottage, included outbuildings where the keepers kept some livestock.

In 1843, Alan succeeded his father as Chief Engineer to the Northern Lighthouse Board.

Ardnamurchan has a visitor's centre with café and car parking, to view the lighthouse you must pay via Admission.

Ardnamurchan lighthouse automated in 1988 monitored by the Northern Lighthouse Board's headquarters in Edinburgh.

Nautical chart position: Latitude 56° 43.6'N, Longitude 6° 13.4'W, type: manned, flashing character 2 white every 30 seconds, fog siren 5 second blasts every 60 seconds, black cupola lantern, platform and balcony-handrail, elevation 55 metres, and nominal range 17 miles.

Bell Rock Lighthouse
Inchcape, North Sea

Robert Stevenson was assistant engineer for the commissioners of Northern Lights during the early stages of building the Bell Rock Lighthouse. When work initially began; at Roberts's suggestion, the commissioners called John Rennie, a Scottish Civil Engineer 1761–1821, into counsel, entrusting him the honorary role of Chief Engineer. During construction, Robert did not accept many of John Rennies proposals, with excessive modifications, design and execution; both men fell into disagreement, leading to Robert Stevenson taking complete control. Stevenson contributed to 18 lighthouses from 1811–1833.

Robert Selkirk, a respected trustee overseen building operations, with production encountering several obstacles, mainly the weather and difficult structural problems. Timescale was unique in that work could only initiate in the summer months when the tide was at it's lowest ebb, over 110 men worked on the construction some lived provisionally on the ship *Smeaton* moored a mile from the Rock, temporary barracks were also affixed. It took four dramatic years for its completion when the lighthouse first commissioned into service, at a cost of £55,619, it had two keepers a third added later, the keepers' families stayed at the Arbroath Signal Tower. On February 1st, Captain John Reid 1811–1819, became the first principal keeper on the Bell Rock.

A Rock Station the Bell Rock lighthouse first exhibited on 1st February, 1811, designed by engineer Robert Stevenson. The structure, a white conical circular tower carved out of granite and sandstone, integrated a succession of bespoke boxed windows. The first 9 metres of three dimensionally interlocking solid dovetail masonry, all 2,500 pieces quarried from Aberdeen, Dundee, and Edinburgh. Remarkably, the first 9 metres of the lighthouse in which half is below high water, there are five chambers enclosed inside, before reaching the lamp room.

The lighthouse is 36 metres in height, 13 metres diameter at the base, tapering into 4.5 metres at the top, the octagonal lantern is finished of with a copper dome, to reach the summit of the tower there are 96 steps, with two small bells positioned either side. Installed inside the tower a clockwork mechanism powering the calibration of weights, enhancing the optical lens system, with a revolving character of 4 to 8 minutes of occurring reflective red and white alternating light emitted introducing the first coloured lights used in character illumination.

Access is by boat, fixed to the Rock is a steel framed grated platform jetty, submerged at high tide, although sometimes provisions dropped by helicopter.

Bell Rock lighthouse became unmanned on the 26th October 1988.

Nautical chart position: Latitude 56º 26.1'N, Longitude 2º 23.1'W, type: manned, flashing characters of white and red, foghorn 2 blasts every 60 seconds, black cupola lantern, platform and balcony-handrail, ironwork balustrade, elevation 28 metres, and nominal range 28 miles.

Buchan Ness

Aberdeenshire

Buchan Ness lighthouse located on a rugged headland next to the picturesque coastal village of Boddam—once a vibrant fishing community with vessels sailing as far as Greenland and Norway—29 miles North of Aberdeen and 3 miles South of Peterhead, in an area of Aberdeenshire with unspoiled, beautiful coastal scenery, and open, raised sea-beaches.

Architectural and Historic interests, in 1819 harbour trustees of Peterhead rallied petitions to the Commissioners to erect a lighthouse on Buchan Ness.

A Rock Station Buchan Ness lighthouse established in 1827 designed by engineer Robert Stevenson.

A single-track road passes over the neatly constructed bridge that separates the Mainland from the Headland; from here, Buchan Ness lighthouse offers overwhelming views across the North Sea. There are 166 steps to reach the lamp room; the lighthouse protected within a red granite boundary wall perimeter, heli-pad nearby, with neatly trimmed lush green lawns.

In 1827, Buchan Ness lighthouse was the first flashing light in Scotland, the constantly rotating light projecting five powerful beams accross the North Sea.

The structure is a round course granite tower, tapering just below the lantern, beautifully crafted arched exposed corbelling stonework, 35 metres in height, eight integrated windows, with two prominent red bands, (painted in 1907), at the base a hemispherical single-storey building, symmetrical keepers cottages positioned either side with eight octagonal red granite chimneys.

Since 1827, the lighting apparatus had several changes to dioptric lens, a globular mirror portioned into fragments generated round a vertical axis. The lantern, distended with increased candlepower from 6,500 to 786,000, converted to electric operation in 1978—with a 100v 3,500w filament bulb increasing candlepower to 2,000,000.

During the Second World War on two separate occasions, mines washed up ashore and exploding causing some damaged to the lighthouse, broken and cracked glass pains, engine room, storehouse roof and surrounding dwellings.

Contractor John Gibb of Aberdeen built the lighthouse; the fog siren now discontinued known locally as the 'Boddam Coo' ended silence in 2000.

Buchan Ness lighthouse, automated in 1988, is now rented out as a holiday home.

Nautical chart position: Latitude 57° 28.2'N, Longitude 01°46.4'W, type: manned, flashing character white every 5 seconds, fog siren 3 blasts of 3 seconds every 90 seconds, black cupola lantern, platform and balcony-handrail, elevation 40 metres, and nominal range 28 miles.

Cape Wrath

Sutherland

Cape Wrath lighthouse looks desolate upon the northwesterly corner of Scotland, when the Norsemen where heading back to there homeland from the 9th to the 15th century, after pillaging and colonizing wide areas of Northern Europe.

Cape Wrath derives from Old Norse word 'Turning Point' when approaching this pointer the Norsemen would navigate their ships round, antagonistic unpredictable waters, where presently the Cape Wrath lighthouse commands respect. Elevated on top of 120 metres above the sea cliffs, and vigilantly overlooking the Atlantic Ocean.

A barren and practically uninhabited remote region with deposits of Old Red Sandstone, the Cape is constrained at certain times of the year due to military exercise operations. To reach the lighthouse, crossing via the Kyle of Durness ferryboat, then travelling a further twelve miles along a not so accessible single-track road.

A Rock Station Cape Wrath Lighthouse established in 1828, designed by engineer Robert Stevenson. John and Alexander Gibb was the contractor for building the lighthouse cost £14,000.

The one-storey keepers' cottage sits adjacent, the structure is granite white painted stone circular tower, with four integrated windows, 20 metres in height, there are 81 steps to reach the lamp room. At the base enclosed a hemispherical single-storey building, encircled within a large boundary wall, the stone used in the lighthouse all quarried nearby from Clash Carnoch.

The light had a paraffin vapour burner, replaced by mercury vapour lamps.

In January 1980, an all electrically operated temporary beam installed at the end of December, a new gearless pedestal and lamp array system fitted.

Stores supplied once a year either by, the Northern Lighthouse Boards' ship MV *Pharos* or by helicopter.

Architectural and Historic interests, Sea cliffs, Stacks and Columns providing perfect sanctuary for a huge colony of birdlife, fulmars, razorbills, puffins, guillemots and kittiwakes. Beyond Cape Wrath and in a direct straight line between these very points lies America.

Cape Wrath lighthouse automated on 31st of March 1998.

Nautical chart position: Latitude 58° 37.5'N, Longitude 5° 59.9'W, type: manned, flashing character 4 white every 30 seconds, fog siren 6 second blast every 90 seconds, black cupola lantern, platform and balcony-handrail, ornamental ironwork balustrade elevation 122 metres, and nominal range 24 miles.

Corsewall
Wigtownshire

After the Bell Rock lighthouse was established in 1811, things became more of less straightforward for Robert Stevenson in the drawing and manufacture of lighthouse engineering.

The Kingdom of the Rhinns in the 11th Century–*Na Renna*, a Norse-Gaelic lordship–appears to have a settlement here. Scottish Gaelic *Na Rannaibh* was a province in medieval Scotland, the definition of the name Corsewall is a place or well of the cross.

A Shore Station Coreswall Lighthouse established in 1817, designed by engineer Robert Stevenson.

The structure is a stone white painted conical tower, a series of eight integrated rectangular and circular windows, 34 metres in height.

Coupled at the base a corbelled castle turret wall in circumference of the tower, the lighthouse enclosed in a efficiently boundary stone perimeter, well intended two-storey keepers' cottages close on adjacent by the tower, the foghorn is now redundant.

There were 45 foghorns in full operation around the 6,158 miles of the Scottish coastline, each giving a unique characteristic deep booming drone between intermittent blasts, as an aid to maritime navigation and to identify their own positions.

Corsewall lighthouse situated at the Northerly Point of the peninsula Corsewall Point Kirkcolm, stretching more than 25 miles from North to South, from here; you get incredible views overlooking the mouth of Loch Ryan in which you can sight the ferries travelling back and forth through the North Channel to Belfast, Northern Ireland.

This is just another fine example of a lighthouse very pleasurable to visit and set within stunning tranquil surroundings.

Corsewall lighthouse automated in 1994, now privately owned and converted into an established hotel.

Nautical chart position: Latitude 55° 00.5'N, Longitude 5° 09.5'W, type: manned. Flashing character, alternative long white and red every 74 Seconds, fog siren 4 blasts every 60 seconds, black cupola lantern, platform and balcony-handrail, ornamental ironwork balustrade, elevation 34 metres, and nominal range 18 miles.

Duncansby Head
Caithness

Duncansby Head Lighthouse placed at the northeast corner of Scotland, a minor road leads from John O'Groats to Duncansby Head, which makes it the furthest point by road from Lands End.

Isolated and exposed to the elements, the lighthouse stands pleasing to the eye overlooking the headland, which prominently encroaches into the North Sea, Pentlands Firth to its North and Moray Firth South.

A Shore Station the Lighthouse established in 1924, designed by engineer David A Stevenson grandson of Robert Stevenson.

The white stone painted tower 11 metres in height, with four integrated windows, painted beige trim all round the perimeter of the building, and attached the one-storey keepers' cottage.

The structure is so dissimilar to the most traditional conical circular lighthouses in that the tower has been designed flushed square, tapering into a medieval castle turret, enclosed within a black lantern being octagon in character there are 31 steps to reach the top of the lamp room.

David contributed to 23 lighthouses from 1892–1937, plus another three with his Uncle, Thomas Stevenson 1885–1886.

During World War II, the lighthouse came under attack, machine-gunned by enemy aircraft; luckily, no one was injured and no damaged caused.

The station also has a foghorn positioned near by; the Pentlands Skerries tidal streams are perilous here because the Atlantic Ocean flows in opposite directions into the North Sea. It ebbs in the opposite direction with dramatic effects sets in motion a welter of eddies, races and overfalls, this creates perilously tidal races in which some have been given names, The Swelkie, Bora of Huna, Wells of Tuftalie, the Duncansby Bore and The Merry Men.

Duncansby Head lighthouse automated in 1997.

Nautical chart position: Latitude 58º 38.6, Longitude 3º 01.4'W, type: manned, flashing character, white every 12 seconds, elevation 67 metres, candlepower 596,000, and nominal range 24 miles.

Dunnet Head

Caithness

Dunnet Head Lighthouse situated 2.35 miles north of John O'Groats, Dunnet Head – Scottish Gaelic: *Ceann Dunaid.*

The lighthouse is positioned on the most northernly point of mainland Britain from here on a clear day panoramic views of the islands of Stroma and Hoy.

Orkney mainland is a distance around 6.75 miles; the point lies in Caithness also known as Easter Head with dramatic cliff-tops descending 105 metres.

During World War II minor defences built to protect naval personnel at Scapa Flow, Orkney.

A Shore Station Dunnet Head established in 1831, designed by engineer Robert Stevenson.

The building contractor was James Smith of Inverness.

The one-storey keepers' cottage, enclosed within a boundary wall, the structure is a stone white circular tower, with five integrated windows, 20 metres in height, at the base a hemispherical single-storeyed building, there are 51 steps and a ladder of 9 runs on it, before reaching the lamp room.

The lantern changed to a dioptric lens in 1852, a combination of lenses with reflectors projecting stronger radiance beam of light, where the original fog signal was positioned, in 1899, due to attrition of the rock, a second fog signal erected, in 1952 a third fog signal installed on top of a small semi-circular tower situated nearby the lighthouse.

Acknowledgment given here to Scots born inventor, Engineer, Robert Foulis who suggests that after hearing his daughter playing the piano in the distance on a foggy night; he noticed a difference in tone, the lower notes were more audible than the higher notes. The outcome giving that low notes can travel a further distance. Foghorns were an admirable navigational aid for mariners especially in, extreme poor visibility conditions, powered by Kelvin diesel engines, a volume of booming compressed air reaching up to 130 Decibels.

Robert also patented a gas light apparatus used in lighthouses.

Due to electronic navigation in the 1980s, the foghorn became redundant replaced by small electric powered sound emitters.

Dunnet Head lighthouse automated on March 1989.

Nautical chart position: Latitude 58° 40.3 'N, Longitude 3° 22.4' W, type: manned, Flashing character 4 white every 30 seconds, fog siren 3 blasts every 90 seconds. Black cupola lantern, platform and balcony-handrail, ornamental ironwork balustrade, elevation 105 metres, and nominal range 26 miles.

Eilean Glas

Scalpay, Western Isles

Eilean Glas Lighthouse – meaning Glas island – Scalpay, is positioned on a small island 300 yards long, 30 metres above Sea level on the Outer Hebrides in the western isles.

A busy shipping lane of the Minch, the lighthouse lies south at Rubh` an Eorna. A pathway across the narrow isthmus* connects Eilean Glas to Scalpay.

A Shore Station Eilean Glas became the fourth lighthouse the commissioners of northern lights sanctioned it has significant value on two accounts.

Firstly, Thomas Smiths proposal of a lighthouse on Scalpay, in that the board of trustees to establish four suitable locations around Scotland, and secondly it was the first lighthouse constructed on the Outer Hebrides.

The lighthouse established in 1789, designed by engineer Thomas Smith. Thomas contributed to 10 lighthouses from 1787–1806.

The one-storey keepers' cottage sits adjacent, within the structure is a stone white circular tower, with nine integrated windows, 30 metres in height, two red bands painted on the tower, distinguished as a day mark.

In 1787 Mr Campbell, a local Tacksman provided building materials and local labour recommended by Captain Alex McLeod of Harris, owner of Scalpay, to oversee the supervision as an interim measure of the work. George Shiells and John William Purdie from Edinburgh the Trustees Stonemasons completed the building work in October 1788.

In 1824, Robert Stevenson erected the present tower; the lightroom raised 7.5 metres, above ground level to the height of 22 metres. A smaller light sits adjacent to the light, which is now redundant.

A fog Signal was installed in 1907 fixed on a semi-circular platform, the revolving light system is catoptric, which is the opposite of dioptric, the (catoptrics), a sealed beam evidently, similar to car headlights, which are mounted on a gearless pedestal, housed behind the lamp or flame to replicate more Candlepower.

Alexander Reid was the first lightkeeper at Eilean Glas Lighthouse and Archie McVicar a joiner from North Uist entrusted with the interior of the building.

Eilean Glas lighthouse automated in 1978 at an operational cost of around £83,565.

Nautical chart position: Latitude 57º 51.4'N, Longitude 6º 38.5'N, type: manned, flashing character 3 whites every 20 seconds, foghorn blast of 4.5 seconds every 45 seconds, black cupola lantern, platform and balcony-handrail, ornamental ironwork balustrade, elevation 43 metres, candlepower 400,000 and nominal range 23 miles.

---

* An isthmus is a narrow strip of land connecting two larger areas.

Esha Ness

Mainland, Shetland Isles

Over the centuries and throughout history, the Shetland Islands an archipelago of 100 islands, stacks, islets and sea-cliffs, became a bargaining proposal between Ancient Kings of Scotland and Norway.

Esha Ness lighthouse located on the Northmavine Peninsula in the Northwesterly side of the Shetland* Islands. Positioned 61 metres above Eshaness dangerously ragged Cliff-tops edge, from here the lighthouse presents spectacular coastal viewpoints, dramatic skylines over the ever-changing Atlantic Skerries.

A Shore Station the lighthouse established in 1929 designed by engineers David Alan Stevenson and Charles Stevenson. Their father David Stevenson was also an Engineer in the family household.

The structure is quite distinctive in that the tower is a well-presented flush-squared masonry white tower, with two integrated windows, 12 metres in height beige trim. The one-storey keepers' cottage stipulated and aligned within the light enclosed around a wired fence rail, the black lantern octagonal in character protected inside a grey iron guardrail. Incompatibilities of local stone the lighthouse being constructed using only concreted materials.

It is worth noting that, Esha Ness only had one keeper during service, while most stations would probably have at least three or four keepers depending on its demanding character and temperament. Between the eighteenth and nineteenth centuries the duties of the keepers did not change very much at all, the customary procedures with trimming of the lamp, the fuel, met reports, cleaning, polishing, painting, rendering walls, stores and repairing fences, the day and night vigilance remaining the same, toiling in all divergent weather conditions became paramount.

When electric light introduced equipment swiftly improved which did have a reflective effect on the keeper's main duties. Amid the nineteenth and twentieth century's things started to transform completely for them, in the development of different light characters, revolving, flashing intermittently, and occulting lights, glass prisms, and technology rapidly advancing, sadly the threat of Automation illuminating over the horizon. The station did have a foghorn but like many others now they have became redundant.

Esha Ness Lighthouse Automated in 1974. The keepers' cottage is available as a holiday home through the Shetland Amenity Trust.

Nautical chart position: Latitude 60° 29.3'N, Longitude 1° 37.6'W, type: manned, flashing character white every 12 seconds, elevation 61 metres, candlepower 46, 5000 and nominal range 25 miles.

---

* During Viking occupation pronounced *Hjatland* Old Norse for mainland.   23

Hyskier Point

Inverness-shire

To caution of shipping at the southern end of the Minch mills rocks, Canna Island and the rock on which the lighthouse is built on.

The name Hyskier, deriving from the Old Norse word *sker* meaning skerry, also *Oigh Sgeir* Scottish Gaelic for 'maiden rock' or 'virgin rock'.

Hyskier is a group of low-lying rocky islets, composed of basalt rock columns, located on a rock 5 miles southwest of the island Canna 8 miles west of Rhum.

Hyskier Island is unoccupied, wildlife in an abundance a popular nesting site for, arctic and common terns, kittiwakes, and eider ducks, basking sharks spotted in the area and large seal colony.

A Rock Station, the lighthouse was established in 1904 designed by engineers David A and Charles Stevenson.

David A Stevenson estimated the cost at £15,134 the work given to Oban Contractor Messrs D & J MacDougall; Chance Brothers fitted the optics costing £821, lanterns, parapet by Dove & Co Edinburgh £1,275.

The one storey-keepers cottage sits adjacent; the structure is a stone white circular tower, with three integrated windows, 39 metres in height 155 steps to reach the lamp room.

The families of the lighthouse keepers lived in Oban, so when the keepers reported for duty they where taken to and from the Lighthouse by helicopter, Heavy-duty apparatus being landed by the Northern Lighthouse Board's Vessel MV *Pharos*.

Hyskier lighthouse automated in March 1997.

Nautical chart position: Latitude 56º 58.2'N, Longitude 6º 40.9'W, type: manned, flashing character 3 white every 30 seconds, black cupola lantern, platform and balcony-handrail, ironwork balustrade, elevation 41 metres, and nominal range 24 miles.

Inchkeith
Fife

Inchkeith is a small island sited on the Firth of Forth's estuary, roughly between Edinburgh and the Kingdom of Fife.

The name Inchkeith derives from *Innse Coit*–meaning 'wooded island'.

Architectural and Historical interest, tells many a story of the Islands folklore past, plagues, sieges, blockades, a medieval fortress, the seat of Pictish Kings and a base for early Christian Evangelists.

The island was attacked during the wars of independence in the 14th century, key battles fought in Lothian and Stirling regions.

A Rock Station the lighthouse established in 1804, designed by engineers, Thomas Smith and Robert Stevenson. Although the lighthouse was built in 1803, it overpowers the small island; it was not until the 14th of September 1804 the lighthouse was established.

The two-storey keepers' cottage coupled within the structure of a rustic stone turret-castle tower, with eight integrated windows, 19 metres in height and 64 steps to reach the lamp room.

The dioptric refracting lens system, first installed at Inchkeith lighthouse in 1835 replacing the catoptrics reflecting system.

In 1899, a new fog signal introduced consisting giving two blasts of 3.5 seconds every, 90 seconds. A diaphone fog signal introduced in 1958, giving 4 blasts each of 1.5 seconds in a rapid succession every 60 seconds.

A Cylinder Piston apparatus device producing, deep powerful audible tones over great lengths in distance.

The Northern Lighthouse sold the island, Inchkeith now privately owned.

Inchkeith lighthouse automated on 1986.

Nautical chart position: Latitude 56° 2.'N, Longitude 3° 8.'W, type: manned, flashing character white every 15 seconds, foghorn 1 blast of 1.5 seconds, every 15 seconds, black cupola lantern, platform and balcony-handrail, ironwork balustrade, elevation 67 metres, candlepower 269,280, and nominal range 23 miles.

Isle of May
Fife

At the mouth of the Firth of Forth's estuary 5 miles from the Fife coastline and 11 miles from East Lothian presents the Isle of May lighthouse. The island is just over a mile long and one-third of a mile wide, made from fine-grained basalt, dark grey colour, tints of greenstone. Architectural and Historic interests, with pilgrimages and ancient burial sites from pagan into Christian times paid homage. St Adrian used the island as a retreat in the ninth century founding a monastic settlement here. King David of Scotland also founded a monastery on the island. King Charles 1st 1635, collected dues from shipping maintenance, first established the Lighthouse. The original 1636 coal fired beacon resembling a medieval castle is still standing nearby the tower. Moreover, in its day, it burned annually 200 tons of coal, set in a brazier or grates, continuous from 1636–1816 and recorded as the oldest lighthouse in Scotland.

An Island Station the lighthouse established in 1816 designed by engineer Robert Stevenson.

The Isle of May lighthouse costing £22,000, the first of many that followed in the progression of electrical technology, improving the light was always primary, on the 1st of December 1886; the Northern Lighthouse Board installed its first electric powered light here.

The structure is quite different, 24 metres in height, a square ornate gothic eerie looking tower, with five integrated semi-archived windows built within a stone dwelling.

The tower attached above at the two-storey keepers' accommodation, three keepers stationed here with a fourth added later. On the 9th of August 1972, the Lighthouse became a Rock Station, which meant that the keeper's families had to live back on the mainland.

The disused low-light lighthouse adjacent to the present tower now used as a bird observatory. Both foghorns positioned either side of the island, fixed on a semi-circular white tower now discontinued.

Accessible by boat, the island now has a heli-pad; the island owned and managed by Scottish National Heritage.

The Isle of May lighthouse automated on the 31st of March 1989.

Nautical chart position: Latitude 56° 11.2'N, Longitude 2° 33.3'W, type: manned, flashing character white every 20 seconds, foghorn 4 blasts every 150 seconds, black cupola lantern, elevation 73 metres, and nominal range of 26 miles.

Kinnaird Head

Fraserburgh

Kinnaird Head (Scottish Gaelic: *An Ceann Ard* meaning the 'High Headland'). When Thomas Smith commissioned four lights at various parts of Scotland, Kinnaird Head was one of these.

Architectural and Historic interests, the Lighthouse situated north of Aberdeenshire. A stronghold for Clan Fraser, towards the close of the 16th centuary, Fraserburgh founded by Sir Alexander Fraser, 8th laird of Philorth built Kinnaird Castle in 1570; the trustees of the Northern Lights turned it into a lighthouse, Kinnaird Head positioned overlooking the harbour.

A Shore Station Kinnaird Head lighthouse established on 1st December 1787 designed by engineer Thomas Smith. When Thomas retired from lighthouse construction to concentrate on his business in Edinburgh, Robert Stevenson went on to succeed him as Chief Engineer of the Northern Lighthouse Board.

James Park, a former mariner, became the first lighthouse keeper at the station. The structure is a white circular tower, 10 metres in height, which sits on top of an old fortified castle, there are 72 steps before you reach the lamproom.

Integrated a series of four commissioned circular windows fitted within the configuration of the lamproom's tower.

In its day Kinnaird Head the most powerful light of its time, with 17 reflectors, in three horizontal tiers. The clockwork mechanism that powered the light was unusual in that it rotated anti-clockwise rather than the normal clockwise. A new lantern put in position in 1824 additional buildings put in place for the first lightkeepers cottages 1851; the fog signal fixed on a semi-circular white tower now discontinued in 1987.

In 1929 Kinnaird Head became home to the first radio beacon in Scotland.

On 19th February 1941, during World War II, two bombs exploded near the lighthouse causing damage to two lenses.

Jim Oliver was the last Principal Lighthouse Keeper at Kinnaird Head.

The original lighthouse at Kinnaird Head is now home to the Museum of Scottish Lighthouses.

Kinnaird Head lighthouse automated in 1991.

Nautical chart position: Latitude 57º 41.9'N, Longitude 2º 0.1'W, type: manned, flashing character white every 15 seconds, foghorn 1 blast every 7 seconds every 1.5 minutes, black cupola lantern, platform and balcony-handrail, ornamental ironwork balustrade, elevation 37 metres, candlepower 690,000, and nominal range 25 miles.

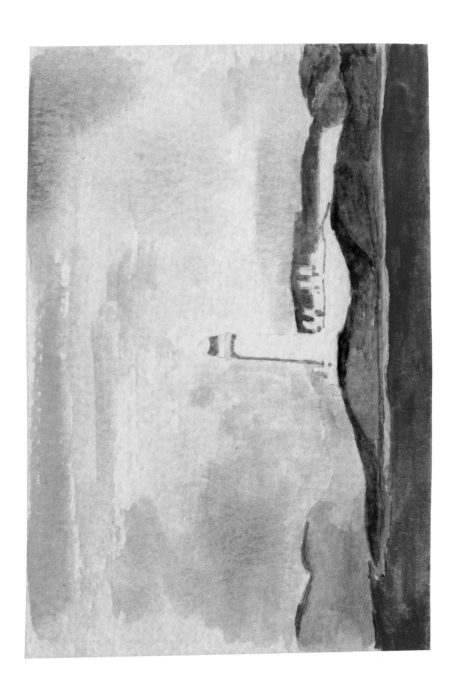

Lismore
Argyllshire

Lismore – *Lios-Mor* in Gaelic – means 'Great Garden' or 'Great Enclosure' sighted on Eilean Musdile in the Firth of Lorne.

The lighthouse detached from Lismore Island by a sound quarter miles broad.

A low-level small island set within beautiful scenic mountains, lismore lighthouse, located in the Inner Hebrides at the entrance of Loch Linnhe. Two ferries, from Oban and Port Appin, service the island.

Historical interests, Lismore compiled of early Iron Age, Christianity and Viking settlements lived contained by this fertile island.

A Rock Station the lighthouse established in 1833, designed by engineer Robert Stevenson. Lismore lighthouse the third constructed that year, Girdle Ness, and Barra Head preceding.

In 1910, The Northern lighthouse Board transformed most of the lighting apparatus to (dioptric) – Lismore and Fidra remained (catoptric) within the service.

The one-storey keepers' cottage enclosed within a boundary wall, the structure is a stone white circular tower, with eight integrated windows, 26 metres in height; at the base a hemispherical single-storey building, overall cost £4,260 to build.

In 1965, the lighthouse converted to Automatic Operational at an estimated added cost of £10,000.

Lismore a Rock Station had four men in total to staff the light, the keepers accommodation positioned behind the tower, enclosed within a boundary wall, the station relived on a fortnightly basis so that the men had six weeks on the rock, two weeks on the mainland with their families.

Robert Selkirk the first Principal Lighthouse Keeper at Lismore.

Oban depot personnel now look after the light.

Lismore lighthouse converted to automatic operation in June 1965.

Nautical chart position: Latitude 56º 27.4'N, Longitude 5º 36.4'W, type: manned, flashing character white every 10 seconds, white cupola lantern, balcony and platform-handrail, ornamental ironwork balustrade, elevation 31 metres, candlepower 71,000 and nominal range 19 miles.

Muckle Flugga

Unst, Shetland Isles

Originally named 'North Unst' but changed to Muckle Flugga in 1964, the name comes from the Old Norse, *Mikla Flugga,* meaning 'Large Steep-Sided Island', one mile north of Unst.

The most Northern summit in the British Isles with the unpredictable chilly Atlantic waters and hereafter the North Pole, Muckle Flugga lighthouse, self-confidently composed, levelled commendably on a perilously serrated rocky cliff top over-looking the Skerries.

A Rock Station the lighthouse established in 1854 designed by engineers Thomas and David Stevenson. Thomas and David Stevenson contributed 28 lighthouses from 1854–1886.

Constructed, mainly for the protection, of Her Majesty's ships during the time of the Crimean War.

The one-storey keeper's cottage sits adjacent, the structure is a brick white circular tower, with four integrated windows; 20 metres in height, there are 71 steps to reach the lamp room.

First exhibited on 1ˢᵗ January in 1858, the lighthouse cost £32,000 in total, the workforces of over 100 men, encountering extreme, harsh labour-intensives with unremarkable methods of using rope, suspended materials and pulling equipment to the summit.

Six lighthouse keepers worked on rotation, three on relive spending one month on, one month off.

The keepers' families based at Hermaness in a two-storey dwelling used as a Shore Station based on Unst, to accommodate the lighthouse keepers when off-duty. The lighthouse was relieved by boat or helicopter .

Robert Louis Stevenson Born Edinburgh 1850, visited Muckle Flugga with his engineering father Thomas Stevenson in 1869, apparently the Island of Unst had an influence with his writing of *Treasure Island.*

Muckle Flugga lighthouse automated in March 1995.

Nautical chart position: Latitude 60° 51.3'N, Longitude 0° 53.'W, type: manned, flashing character 2 white every 20 seconds, black cupola lantern, platform and balcony-handrail, ironwork balustrade, elevation 66 metres, and nominal range 25 miles.

Mull of Galloway

Wigtownshire

The most southerly point of the Scottish mainland, Mull of Galloway lighthouse placed prominently elevated on the Rhinns of Galloway Headland. Towering vigilantly above sea level, the lighthouse sits over-looking the North Channel and the Irish Sea. The sea cliffs provide the perfect sanctuary for birdlife population here, 76 metres drops, the area, a haven for guillemots, razorbills, and puffins all finding perfect sanctuary within cliff-top ledges, protected by the RSPB.

Even on a hot summers day the weather conditions can change quite dramatically, low level flying clouds appearing from nowhere, which can make it very blustery on the peninsula, on a clear day you get awesome panoramic views over to England, the Isle of Man, and the Emerald Isle.

A Shore Station the Lighthouse established in 1830, designed by Engineer Robert Stevenson. The cost of the lighthouse was between £8,000 and £9,000 pounds, Contractor Brebner & Scott of Edinburgh

The one-storey keepers cottages enclosed within the boundary walls, the structure is a stone white circular tower, with eight integrated windows, 26 metres in height, at the base a hemispherical single-storey building. There are 114 steps to reach the lamp room. The foghorn now discontinued.

The PLK (salary £45 per year) two assistants and their families lived in the one storey keepers cottages nearby, paddock for grazing, the surrounding out-buildings contained engine room, ash pit, workshop, stores, oil and coal.

In 1971 the lamp converted to electric, with a sealed-beam mounted on a gearless revolving pedestal. This apparatus was convenient to install and simple to maintain. Within the service, different variations and characteristics of lights were developing such as "intermittent" or "occulting" flashing lights projecting in obscured weather conditions. A heli-pad is in close proximity to the lighthouse.

The keeper's cottages, have been converted into holiday homes for rent, through The National Trust for Scotland.

Adjacent to the light, the Mull of Galloway has a visitor's centre, from the Northern Lighthouse Board's web site, a live web-cam positioned inside the lamp room, gives all-round dynamic views of the Irish Sea.

Mull of Galloway lighthouse demanned in 1988.

Nautical chart position: Latitude 54° 38.1'N, Longitude 4° 51.4'W, type: manned, flashing character white every 30 seconds, fog siren 2 blasts every 60 seconds, black cupola lantern, platform and balcony-handrail, ornamental ironwork balustrade, elevation 99 metres, and nominal range 28 miles.

Mull of Kintyre
Argyllshire

The term Mull–*Maol*–Gaelic meaning, 'rounded hill' or open summit; *Maol Ceanntire* the destination for Scots coming across from Ireland, to reach the Kingdom of Dal Riata, modern day Argyll.

Mull of Kintyre Lighthouse second light in Scotland for the commissioner's remit, North Ronaldsay, and Eilean Glas following a year later.

Positioned on the southernmost point of this breathtaking peninsula concealed into coarse open moorland, with dangerously twisted curvature bends appears the Gap to the lighthouse, sitting gracefully in attendance overlooking the North Channel.

On a clear day, the Mountainous Peaks of Arran, Aisla Craig and the Antrim Coast of Northern Ireland come into view.

A Shore Station the Lighthouse first exhibited on 1ˢᵗ November 1788 established and designed by Engineer Thomas Smith, assistance from his young apprentice stepson Robert Stevenson. It took 22 months for its completion, under extremely difficult circumstances, equipment-building provisions where landed by boat 6 miles away, then transported on horseback over a mountainous path, each limited load calculated as 1cwt (50 kilo) in weight.

Mull of Kintyre lighthouse cost £9,000 the Contractors involved were George Shiells a stonemason for the Trustees, Messrs Chance Brothers Birmingham and Messrs James Dove & Co. Edinburgh.

The one-storey keepers' cottages enclosed within a boundary wall, the structure is a yellow conical circular tower, integrated a sequence of windows, 12 metres in height, 15 steps to reach the lamp-room, the station also had a fog-signal fixed upon a brick tower, close by a heli-pad.

Matthew Hardie became the first lighthouse keeper at the Mull of Kintyre, with payment of £50 pound per annum.

The keeper's cottages been converted into holiday homes for rent, through the National Trust for Scotland.

Mull of Kintyre lighthouse automated in 1996.

Nautical chart position: Latitude 55º 18.6'N, Longitude 5º 48.1'W, type: manned, flashing character 2 white every 20 seconds, foghorn 2 blasts every 90 seconds, black cupola lantern, platform and balcony-handrail, ironwork balustrade, elevation 91 metres, and nominal range 29 miles.

Noss Head

Caithness

Noss deriving from the Old Norse word meaning 'Nose of the land' or 'Point'; Noss Head lighthouse positioned three miles outside the town of Wick in Caithness. Castle Sinclair and Girnigoe Castle built around the 14th to 17th centuaries home of the Sinclair Family Earl of Caithness.

A Shore Station the lighthouse established in 1849, designed by engineer Alan Stevenson.

The one-storey keepers' cottage sits adjacent, the structure is a stone white short circular tower, with six integrated windows, 18 metres in height; at the base enclosed a hemispherical single-storeyed building, there is 76 steps to reach the lamp room.

The building contractor was Robert Arnott of Inverness, Egyptian style architecture incorporated in the drawing within the keepers' cottages.

Alan's close Association with the Fresnels brothers, Augustin and Lenoir who where the pioneers in the projection with lenses, reflectors, glass prisms.

Improving the light became paramount; Alan kept a good working relationship with Augustin and Lenoir, the French inventors proved to be encouraging; eventually the candlepower in the Scottish lighthouses became the most powerful in the world.

First exhibited on Monday 18th June 1849 instead of the traditional upright black ironwork framing incorporated within the lantern, Alan introduced a new diagonal design at Noss Head, providing a much stronger light, less prone to change or interruption on any bearing.

The lighthouse now privately owned.

Noss Head lighthouse automated in 1987.

Nautical chart position: Latitude 58º 28.8'N, Longitude 3º 03.'W, type: manned, flashing character white / red every 20 seconds, black cupola lantern, platform and balcony-handrail, ironwork balustrade, elevation 53 metres, and nominal range white 25 miles, red 21 miles.

Ornsay
Skye

Ornsay Lighthouse situated on a tidal rock southeast of the Sound of Sleat, a small Island accessible at low tide south of Colonsay, the Isle of Skye's mystical mountains providing the perfect scenic backdrop.

Oronsay – Scottish Gaelic: *Ora Saigh* – the name comes from *Orfirirsey* which translates from Old Norse 'tidal island' or 'ebb island'.

A Rock Station the lighthouse established in 1857 designed by engineers David and Thomas Stevenson. David and Thomas Stevenson now successfully cementing a strong partnership in the world of lighthouse construction, with brother Alan's health not improving, David in due course went on to succeed Alan in 1853 as Chief Engineer for the Commissioners of the Northern Lights, establishing a further potential 45 locations for lights around the Coast of Scotland.

Thomas Stevenson contributed 28 lighthouses 1854–1886 plus 3 with his nephew David A Stevenson.

Positioned on the adjacent islet, Eilean Sionnach; the structure is a stone white circular tower, with four integrated windows, 19 metres in height.

In improving the dioptric lens at Ornsay, Thomas devised a new condensing apparatus diversed in various strengths, showing different focal directions from the distance, which is necessary to view.

In the event of mains power failure, Ornsay lighthouse has battery back up for fourteen days operation of emergency light.

The principal lightkeeper and his assistants would live in the two pitched roof cottages on the Island; the light powered by gas, which delivered by the Northern Lighthouse Board's supply vessel MV *Pharos*.

The keepers given twelve gas cylinders a year, in 1988 the light was modernised by electric when mains power replaced the previous gas system.

The two keepers' cottages have been altered into one dwelling.

Ornsay lighthouse automated in 1962.

Nautical chart position: Latitude 57° 8.6'N, Longitude 5° 46.4'W, type: manned, flashing character 2 white every 7 seconds, black cupola lantern, platform and balcony-handrail, ironwork balustrade, elevation 18 metres, and nominal range 12 miles.

Out Skerries

Whalsay, Skerries, Shetland Isles

The Out Skerries are a small group of habited islands located on Shetland's most eastern area of Scotland. Positioned more or less 24 miles North East from Lerwick, a collection of three main islands found in the North Sea.

Forming Housay, Bruary and Grunary a population of less than one hundred scattered throughout the landscape.

Housay island a rich resource of geographical mineral deposits granite, limestone, gneiss and schist. Bruary has the smallest school in Scotland.

The keepers' former living accommodation on the nearby island of Grunary now un-habited except for sheep, an unbelievable array of bird's and wonderful wildlife colonel, seals, otters, exploring these beautiful and rugged wind washed islands.

A Rock Station the lighthouse established in 1854 designed by engineers David and Thomas Stevenson.

The structure a round brick white circular tower, with five integrated windows, 30 metres in height; the lighthouse is impressive towering above the Islands.

The original lighting apparatus fixed as a Dalen light, distinguished of its (Solar Valve) Calcium Carbide with water, the light motorized by Acetylene gas, the lens up-graded to electric drive with a metal halide (35 watt) lamp in 2000.

Throughout World War II, lighthouses were a constant target for enemy aircraft bombers, attempts where made to destroy the Out Skerries lighthouse.

Some of the lighthouse internal buildings were machine-gunned, the boatman's wash house, coal stores took a direct hit, his mother being the inhabitant at the time, was buried underneath the wreckage, She never survived this tragedy.

Alan Brebner of Edinburgh had overseen the building of the lighthouse cost £21,000.

Out Skerries lighthouse on bound skerry is Accessible only by boat, the adjoining islands Housay and Bruary are concurrent by a small bridge.

The Shetland Islands accommodated by excellent ferry links with inner and outer flight services.

Out Skerries lighthouse was automated and demanned in April 7ᵗʰ 1972.

Nautical chart position: Latitude 60° 25.5'N, Longitude 0° 43.5'N, type: manned, flashing character white every 20 seconds, foghorn 2 blasts every 45 seconds, black cupola lantern, platform and balcony-handrail, ironwork balustrade, elevation 44 metres, candlepower 159,000, and nominal range 20 miles.

Pladda

Arran

Positioned in the Firth of Clyde Pladda – Scottish Gaelic: *Pladaigh* – is a small verdant green island off the south east coast corner of Arran, with its rain-drop or tear-shaped appearance, here Pladda lighthouse standing firmly alone, bordered by a stone wall perimeter.

After the first four lights were completed, Pladda was next, Commissioned by the board of trustees of the Northern Lights, Pladda lighthouse the first constructed on the Clyde, also the third station to have a fog signal installed in 1786.

Originally, a Rock Station the lighthouse established in 1790, designed by engineer Thomas Smith.

The one-storey keeper's cottage sits adjacent, the structure is a stone white circular tower, with nine integrated windows, 29 metres in height; two pitched roof buildings, there are 128 steps to reach the lamp room.

Pladda low lighthouse neighbouring to the main light on the island, dates are unknown however, and the little tower was active for more than 100 years.

Supplies brought over to the lighthouse by boatmen permanently attached to the station; in 1972, a helicopter service introduced to transport the keepers back and forward; in 1815 the board employed assistant lightkeepers into the service, with many stations now having a principal lightkeeper and two assistants with their families living nearby in the cottages provided.

Pladda Lighthouse, complementing within its natural setting, distinguished two lights.

Pladda lighthouse automated in 1990.

Nautical chart position: Latitude 55º 25.5'N, Longitude 5º 07.3'W, type: manned, flashing character 3 white every 30 seconds, fog siren 2 blasts every 20 seconds, black cupola lantern, platform and balcony-handrail, ornamental ironwork balustrade, elevation 40 metres, and nominal range of 23 miles.

Rinns of Islay
Argyllshire

Orsay – Scottish Gaelic: *Orasaigh* – is a small island of the South West Coast of Islay, populated with wildlife, you can watch seals resting on the rocks. The picturesque postcard village of Portnahaven by the small harbour provides the visitor with breathtaking scenery, *Rinn* – Gaelic for 'point' or Gaelic *Rann*.

Modern day Islay has a population of 3,000 inhabitants. Known as the Queen of the Hebrides where once the Kings and Queens of ancient Gaelic and Celtic cultures held court.

This rugged coastline - a hazardous passage for any mariner - has dangerous undercurrents and whirlpools, responsible for many shipwrecks.

Recognized as a Rock Station the lighthouse established in 1825, designed by engineer Robert Stevenson.

The structure a stone white circular tower, incorporated with a sequence of well crafted circular and rectangle windows, 29 metres in height, there are 131 steps to reach the lamp room, at the base a hemispherical single-storey building.

The one-storey keeper's cottages accommodation; positioned symmetrically either side of the light, enclosed by boundary walls.

The original Paraffin light lens system needed turned by the keepers constantly every 45 minutes for the clockwork mechanism to rewind.

John Gibb of Aberdeen was the Contractor for this impressive configuration with a cost of building the lighthouse between £8,000 and £9,000 pounds.

Boatmen permanently assigned to the station brought over equipment, stores and other provisions via boat to the Island, they also did reliefs.

Lightkeepers duties were ongoing, with not just the supervision of the lantern and the light room, key responsibilities included all year round maintenance and upkeep of the station. Daily routine would include inspections of all apparatus, stores, fuel, daily-reports, cleaning, and painting, ensuring everything was kept spotless, and even that the lawns were kept neatly trimmed.

The commissioners visited the lights once a year for their annual inspection tour they also overseen the daily management of the lighthouse service in Scotland.

Rinns of Islay lighthouse automated on 31ˢᵗ March 1998.

Nautical chart position: Latitude 55° 40.4'N, Longitude 6° 30.8'W, type: manned, flashing character white every 5 seconds, fog siren 3 blasts every 90 seconds, black cupola lantern, platform and balcony-handrail, ornamental ironwork balustrade, elevation 46 metres, and nominal range 24 miles.

M·MACPHERS...

Rubh' Re

Wester Ross-shire

This impressive remote peninsula – Scottish Gaelic: *Rubha Rèidh* meaning 'smooth headland' – concealed away in the North West corner of the Scottish mainland is active with marine and bird wildlife, scenic mountains and unspoiled beaches.

Rubh' Re lighthouse affords breathtaking views of the Isle of Skye, Rona and Western Isles over the North Minch.

Originally, a Shore Station the lighthouse first exhibited on 15th January 1912 established and designed by engineer David Alan Stevenson.

The station cost £14,900 with the Board of Trade authorising the payments.

The two-storey keepers' cottages sit enclosed within a boundary wall, changed to a Rock Station in 1962, the structure is a stone white attached circular tower, with five integrated windows, 25 metres in height, enclosed within a boundary wall, there are 87 steps before reaching the lamp room.

As a means of generating, a good source of powerful light for the lighthouse, experimentation using different types of fuels such as coal, colza oil, sperm whale oil, paraffin, gas and electricity, were tried in the early days.

Aime Argand, born in Switzerland in 1755, was a physicist and chemist; in 1784, he invented the Argand Burner oil lamp, which brought forward a completely new perception into the world of lighthouse lantern clarification.

In 1912, the station had a fog signal introduced. The fog signal fell silent from service in 1980, now redundant, with the removal of equipment in 1985.

The Gairloch Heritage Museum now exhibit the foghorn, clockwork mechanism, and lens and lighting apparatus.

The completion of a new single-track road surface gave much easier access to the lighthouse, before this the only accessible route was on foot or by boat.

Rubh' Re lighthouse converted into a Guest House.

Rubh' Re lighthouse automated in 1986.

Nautical chart position: Latitude 57° 51.41'N, Longitude 5° 48.6'W, type: manned, flashing character 4 white every 15 seconds, black cupola lantern, platform and balcony-handrail, ironwork balustrade, elevation 37 metres, and nominal range 23 miles.

Saint Abbs Head

Berwickshire

In 1857, after the sinking of the *Martello* on Carr rock the Northern Lighthouse Board recommended the construction of a lighthouse on St Abbs Head.

To aid navigational shipping, for monitoring other lights on the Firth of Forth, the lighthouse used as communications control station before and after the sight of the Bell Rock, Bass Rock and Isle of May lights was lost.

A Shore Station the Lighthouse first exhibited on February 24th 1862 designed and established by engineers David & Thomas Stevenson.

The two storey keepers cottages sit advanced above sheltered within a neatly built boundary walled perimeter, over looking the lighthouse and fog siren below.

The structure is a short white tower of 9 metres in height, the lighthouse situated on the edge of a jagged 91.5 metres cliff top drop.

In 1876, the board installed its first foghorn siren at St Abbs Head.

Originally power-driven by Compressed Hot Air, and then in 1911 motorized by Oil-Fluid, in 1955 the foghorn apparatus converted to Kelvin diesel powered engines.

In 1987, the Foghorn discontinued from service.

Three keepers and their families lived here, to gain access to the lamp room they would go through a wrought iron gate, descend the steep stairs, which fixed secured by an outside edge wall and handrail.

Previously the lights power source by Oil and Incandescent illumination, in 1966 the lights emissions changed to electric.

The area around St Abbs head is a National Nature Reserve managed by the National Trust for Scotland. Razorbills, shags, kittiwakes, puffins, fulmars, and guillemots, are all in clear view, with the sea cliffs providing perfect protection for birdlife.

There is a circular walk popular with hill walkers that includes the lighthouse.

St Abbs Head lighthouse automated in 1993.

Nautical chart position: Latitude 55º 55.'N, Longitude 2º 8.3'W, type: manned, flashing character white every 10 seconds, fog siren 1 blast every 45 seconds, black cupola lantern, elevation 68 metres, and nominal range 29 miles.

Sanda

Kintyre, Argyllshire

Blended magnificently into its natural surroundings of the rock facade, the islands geology is lower old red sandstone in red and yellow varieties and undifferated schists (metamorphic rocks).

Sanda lighthouse situated off the south end of the Kintyre peninsula on a small island of the North Channel between Scotland and Ireland. Sanda – Scottish Gaelic: *Sandaigh* – the island has historic connections with several personages. Robert the Bruce, William Wallace, Saint Ninian, it said that Saint Ninian buried here.

A Rock Station the lighthouse established in 1850 designed by engineer Alan Stevenson.

The structure is a stone white circular tower 15 metres in height, with three integrated windows, with a one-storey keeper's cottage. The the lighthouse is perfectly balanced on the small summit of Prince Edwards Rock.

Alan Stevenson has managed to achieve a striking contrast here, incorporated into the Rock-Face, are two elegant complimentary stone brick towers, with 11 well-dressed windows, ascending 210 steps before reaching the lamp room.

Sanda lighthouse nicknamed the ship, when viewed from the seat of the south the natural arch, the lighthouse on the rock can resemble the shape of a ship.

A heli-pad built in close proximity the light, in 1976-77, a helicopter service first introduced to convey the relief of the lighthouse keepers, who where originally relieved by boat.

Sanda lighthouse automated in 1993.

Nautical chart position: Latitude 55° 16.5'N, Longitude 5° 34.9'W, type: manned, long flashing character white/red every 24 seconds, fog siren 1 blast every 7 seconds every 60 seconds, black cupola lantern, platform and balcony-handrail, ironwork balustrade, elevation 50 metres, and nominal range white 19 miles, red 16 miles.

Scurdie Ness
Montrose

The Angus Coastal trail offers fantastic scenery, breathtaking open views, birds, wildlife, seals, and local history in abundance with heritage pocketed along the rugged coastal cliffs throughout this never-ending Headland.

At the entrance to the Montrose basin south of the mouth of the River Esk, pass through the picturesque fishing village of Ferryden, along a single track road, Scurdie Ness lighthouse comes into view situated on the East Coast of the Scottish Mainland.

Architectural and Historic interests, Volcanic in structure the landscape rich in raw materials with various resourceful deposits of minerals, old red sandstone, basalt, sedimentary, orthopyroxene-feldspar.

The Northern Lighthouse Board, commissioned to erect a lighthouse between the Bell Rock and Girdle Ness lights after a high volume of shipwrecks with considerable great loss of life.

A Shore Station Scurdie Ness lighthouse first exhibited on Tuesday 1st March in 1870, designed and established by engineers David & Thomas Stevenson.

The lighthouse and the keepers' pitched roof cottages and outbuildings enclosed and composed within the grounds. The structure is a stone white circular tower, 39 metres in height, 170 steps to reach the lamp room.

Colossal in stature, this outstanding lighthouse, erected on the edge of the embankment, has open views over the Angus headland and onto the North Sea. Integrated within the tower are nine well-fitted rectangular windows, with a neatly finished circular ironwork hand-rail positioned outside the landing platform and balcony.

On a very clear day, you can see for miles, even as far as Berwick.

Scurdie Ness Automated in 1987.

Nautical chart position: Latitude 56° 42.1'N, Longitude 2° 26.1'W, type: manned, flashing character 3 every 30 seconds, black cupola lantern, platform and balcony-handrail, ironwork balustrade, elevation 38 metres, candlepower 182,000, and nominal range 21 miles.

Originally, a fixed white light in character but changed in 1907 to isophane white every 60 seconds (light 30 seconds, eclipse 30 seconds).

Skerryvore

Argyllshire

Derived from the Gaelic word *Sgeir Mhor* meaning 'big' or 'big rock' situated 12 miles off the west coast of Tiree, Skerryvore lighthouse is standing perceptibly on a treacherous rocky reef.

A Rock Station the lighthouse established in 1844, designed by engineer Alan Stevenson. Alan Stevenson was aged just 30 when he presented Skerryvore into the World of lighthouse engineering, facing harsh weather conditions, disastrous setbacks after setbacks; achieving the impossible, like his father beforehand, on the "Bell Rock" to belief that it was not feasible to establish a lighthouse on the perilous reef. Skerryvore lighthouse took six years for its completion from 1838–1844, the workmen being based at Hynish, barracks were also erected on the reef which became temporary accommodation for the labour force, the first three courses at the base of the lighthouse tower are hard Hynish Gneiss with the remainder being quarried from the Earraid Ross of Mull.

The structure is grey granite circular tower, integrated a progression of petite boxed windows, 48 metres in height, there are 151 steps to the reach lamp room. The tallest and heaviest lighthouse in the United Kingdom cost overall £72,200. Its structure weighs a staggering 4,308 tons. Amongst its ranks, 48 metres in diameter, 13 metres at the base of the tower with 3 metre thick granite blocks, tapering into 5 metres at the lantern with 0.6 metre blocks at the top. Three keepers lived here within eleven apartments each 4 metres in diameter.

The lighthouse severely damaged by fire on March 16th 1954 it took four years before men staffed the light, thankfully no one was hurt. In the provisional period, a temporary automatic Dalen light positioned on the rock.

In 1972, a helicopter pad constructed with additional fuel storage tanks.

The keepers' families and stores buildings based at Hynish, 10.5 miles southwest of the Isle of Tiree.

Jim Cummings who worked as a Stonemason at Skerryvore was the first Principal Lighthouse Keeper here.

In 1984, the old signal tower at Hynish successfully been converted into the Skerryvore lighthouse Museum.

Skerryvore lighthouse, the very last foghorn switched off in Scotland on 4th October 2005.

Skerryvore lighthouse automated in 1994.

Nautical chart position: Latitude 56º 19.4'N, Longitude 7º 6.9'W, type: manned, flashing character white every 10 seconds, foghorn 1 blast every 60 seconds, black cupola lantern, platform and balcony-handrail, ironwork balustrade, elevation 46 metres, and nominal range 26 miles.

Stoer Head

Ru Stoer, Sutherland

Marking the headland of the point of Stoer on the West Coast of Scotland, the Ru Stoer lighthouse also known as Stoer Head elevated 54 metres above sea level, another fine example of Stevenson engineering at its best.

Excellent coastal scenery, dramatic sunsets, with marine and wildlife in abundance the light positioned pleasantly watching over the ever-changing North Minch.

A Shore Station the lighthouse established in 1870 designed by engineers David and Thomas Stevenson.

The structure is a stone white circular tower, with three integrated windows, 14 metres in height, the lighthouse and the two storey-keepers' cottages are enclosed in a neatly built stonewall perimeter.

The principal lightkeeper with one assistant and their families stayed at the station in the two houses next to the tower, they were quite self-sufficient in growing there own food, with livestock sheltering in the near by stable and cowshed, all built within the station.

When the keepers were on duty they took turns in trimming lamp wicks every four hours so that the light would burn consistently throughout the hours of darkness.

The lamp is now electric an array of sealed-beam electric lamps, a light sensor switches automatically on and off when daylight falls and rises between set periods of the day.

The lightkeepers cottages converted into holiday homes for rent, through the National Trust for Scotland.

Stoer Head lighthouse automated in 1978.

Nautical chart position: Latitude 58° 14.4'N, Longitude 5° 24.'W, type: manned, flashing characters white every 15 seconds, black cupola lantern, platform and balcony-handrail, ironwork balustrade, elevation 59 metres, and nominal range 24 miles.

Stroma
Caithness

Stroma Scottish Gaelic *Sromaigh* is a small island off the Northern-most point of the Scottish Mainland, situated in the Pentland Firth between Orkney and Caithness, the channel that separates Orkney from the Mainland, deriving from the Old Norse word *Straum-oy* meaning 'Island in the Tidal Stream'.

The Swilkie whirlpool ebbs and flows with dangerous tidal races in the Pentland Firth, which is present at both the North and South end of the Island.

Originally, a Shore Station the lighthouse established in 1896 designed by engineers David A & Charles Stevenson.

The structure is a stone white circular tower, with five integrated windows; 23 metres in height, there are 80 steps to reach the lamp room, at the base of the tower attached a small single storey building.

The station did have a Fog Signal, which has now become redundant the two circular white towers varied in height stand outside the compounds of the lighthouse grounds.

On the 22nd of February 1941, during World War II, the lighthouse buildings were machine-gunned by enemy aircraft, no one was injured and the keepers repaired what little damaged had been done.

The lighthouse remained a Shore Station until 1961; now a Rock Station. Three keepers lived here in the one-storey cottages enclosed within a fortified boundary wall, they worked four weeks on followed by four weeks off.

In 1972, Stroma lighthouse converted to electric operation, in 1994, work commenced in April to convert the station to automatic operation, the sealed beamed lamp array optic was replaced and removed by the Sule Skerry 4th order lens system. This rotates using a gearless pedestal and the light source is a 250W metal halide lamp. A helicopter pad built near the station to facilitate maintenance work and the changeover of relief for the keepers.

Accessible by boat the Island is now uninhabited the last family leaving in 1962.

Stroma lighthouse automated in 1997.

Nautical chart position: Latitude 58° 41.8'N, Longitude 3° 7.'W, type: manned, flashing character 2 white every 20 seconds, foghorn 2 blasts every 60 seconds, black cupola lantern, platform and balcony-handrail, ironwork balustrade, elevation 32 metres, and nominal range 26 miles.

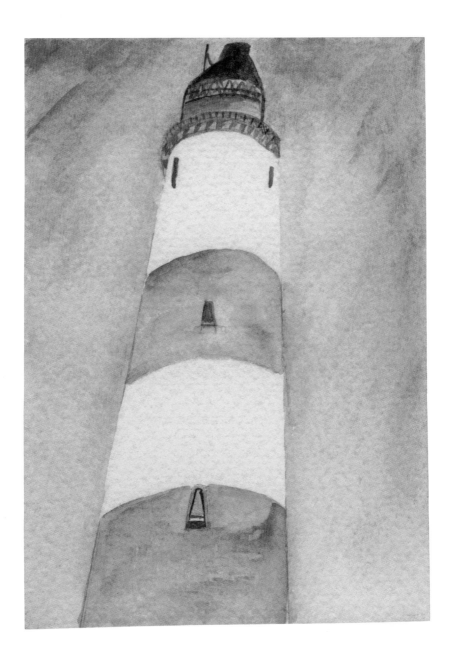

Tarbat Ness

Ross & Cromarty

Tarbat Ness Lighthouse with its distinctive two red bands stands regimentally looking over the Moray Firth, the lighthouse is of architectural interest and the third tallest in Scotland, (North Ronaldsay and Skerryvore being taller).

An architectural interest, the Peninsula is mainly composed of farmland; with sedimentary rock structures weathering in calciferous rock; it also has significant geological and ornithological importance.

Migratory birds use Tarbat Ness as a stopping of point during the autumn migration, with particular interest of seabirds passing through the Moray Firth. A Shore Station the lighthouse first exhibited on 26ᵗʰ January 1830 established and designed by engineer Robert Stevenson.

The navigational light an Argand Paraffin lamp four burners operated until 1907 when it changed to an incandescent pressurised lamp with 55 mantles.

The lens and machinery, installed in 1892, remained in use until major automation in 1985. The old lens and machinery apparatus are now exhibited in the National Maritime Museum, Greenwich.

The structure is a brick conical imposing tower 41 metres in height, at the base enclosed a hemispherical single-storey building, there are 203 steps to reach the lamp room; with thirteen integrated rectangle windows fitted sporadically around the tower, giving all round significant views.

Tarbat Ness is enclosed, within a stonewall perimeter with the one-storey keepers' cottages and out buildings nearby.

James Smith of Inverness was the contractor responsible for the lighthouse, cost £9,361 and bears two distinctive broad red bands.

The site where the lighthouse is built was, according to local folklore, a meeting place for witches' covens and - prior to that - an old Roman Fort.

Three keepers and their families lived at the station, before automation, the last Principal Keeper here was Jack Clark.

Tarbat Ness Lighthouse automated in 1985.

Nautical chart position: Latitude 57° 51.9'N, Longitude 3° 46.5'W, type: manned, flashing character 4 white every 30 seconds, black cupola lantern, platform and balcony-handrail, ornamental ironwork balustrade, elevation 53 metres, and nominal range 24 miles.

Tod Head
Aberdeenshire

On the 8ᵗʰ November 1894, the board of trade sanctioned to build a lighthouse and fog signal on a Headland between Montrose and Stonehaven.

Architectural and Historic interests, Tod Head lighthouse is a listed building.

From landward Tod Head lighthouse is most visible from the Aberdeen Coastal Route when heading southward. It sits overlooking the North Sea, impeccably elevated above the clifftop, with lush green farmland in the background.

David A Stevenson contributed to 26 lighthouses from a period 1885–1937.

A Shore Station the lighthouse established in 1897, designed by engineer David A. Stevenson.

The structure is stone white circular tower, with three integrated windows, adjacent to the one-storey building; the foghorn came into operation on 28ᵗʰ April 1898.

The two-storey keepers' cottages enclosed in a boundary wall perimeter, other outbuildings providing washing facilities and coal stores.

John Mitchell & Sons of Edinburgh were responsible for the building of the light, which cost £4,828 3/9d, inside the tower before reaching the lightroom, the interior walls dressed in immaculate white flagstone tiling, a cantilevered stone stairwell incorporated in the design, solid wood hand banister rail and a black cast iron staircase.

Other cost incurred for various parts of equipment, apparatus, machinery, with the overall total estimate of £10,378.

In 1973, a large electric lamp fitted to re-place the existing paraffin vapour burner, the foghorn re-produced to activate automatically when visibility falls below a certain variety.

In January 2005, the General Lighthouse Authorities (GLAs)–Trinity House Lighthouse Service, the Northern Lighthouse Board and the Commissioners of the Irish Lights, reviewed aids of navigation around the coast of the United Kingdom and Ireland.

The outcome of this consultation agreed to discontinue. Therefore, Tod Head permanently switched off with effect from the 11ᵗʰ July 2007.

Tod Head lighthouse automated in 1988.

Nautical chart position: Latitude 56° 53.'N, Longitude 2° 12.8'W, type: manned, flashing character 4 white every 30 seconds, foghorn 4 blasts every 60 seconds, black cupola lantern, platform and balcony-handrail, ironwork balustrade, elevation 41 metres, candlepower 3,000,000, and nominal range 29 miles.